HÄGAR®

THE HORRIBLE

C000115589

©1995 King Features Syndicate Inc.

Published by

Pedigree
BOOKS

Pedigree Books Limited
The Old Rectory,
Matford Lane, Exeter,
Devon, EX2 4PS.

ISBN 1.874507.50.3
Printed in Italy

£4.95

HA 1

HAGAR'S PHILOSOPHY IS: "BE ALL YOU CAN BE..."

...I'D SAY HE HAS ABOUT ANOTHER 25 POUNDS TO GO

CHOMP! CHOMP!

WHEN I'M ON A DIET EVERYTHING I SEE MAKES ME THINK OF SOMETHING GOOD TO EAT!!

LIKE WHAT?

CHOCOLATE MARSHMALLOW SUNDAES!

POLLY WANTS A CRACKER

AH-AH! HOW DO WE ASK?

PLEASE?

VERY GOOD!

I LIKE IT BETTER WHEN HAGAR'S HOME

58

59

HAGAR HAS A NASTY COLD, DR. ZOOK, BUT AS USUAL HE'S HANDLING IT VERY WELL

GOOD

...NOW IF YOU'LL JUST TAKE HIS TEDDY BEARS, I'LL EXAMINE HIM

CHRIS BROWNE

1-2

WHAT'S IN THIS BLUE BOTTLE?

THAT'S MY BATH SALTS AND KEEP YOUR HANDS OFF IT!

SORRY

CHRIS BROWNE
1-28

HAGAR, ARE YOU GOING TO HANG THIS PICTURE FOR ME?

I'M GETTING MY TOOLS

CHRIS BROWNE

WHERE DO YOU WANT IT HUNG?

1-29

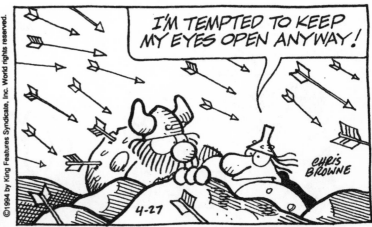

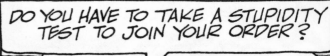

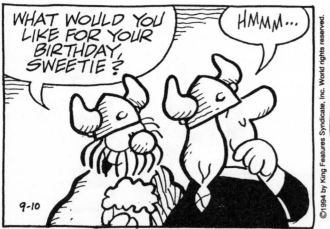

LIKE IT? IT STARTED OUT TO BE A TORTURE RACK! BUT AT SOME POINT IT TURNED INTO AN *EXERCISE MACHINE!*

CHRIS BROWNE

9-22

I BATHE SNERT EVERY MONDAY AND EVERY WEDNESDAY, BUT BY FRIDAY NIGHT HIS FLEAS ARE GOING *WILD!*

AND WHO CAN BLAME THEM?

IT'S THE *WEEKEND!*

CHRIS BROWNE

9-23

REMEMBER— YOU GOTTA LOOK OUT FOR NUMBER *ONE!*

RIGHT!

9-24

WHAT'S HE LOOK LIKE?

CHRIS BROWNE

I THINK I JUST INVENTED BODY PIERCING

59

UH-OH...DID I MISS A MEETING?

A WISE MAN SAID, "HE WHO STAYS OUT LATE AND SPENDS HIS MONEY ON DEVIL'S RUM MUST BE PREPARED TO DO WITHOUT"

DO WITHOUT WHAT?

DINNER